# Disney PRINCESS

# Enchanting Story

Read the story, then flip the book over
to find spellbinding activities!

By Barbara Bazaldua
Illustrated by Denise Shimabukuro and Studio IBOIX

First published by Parragon in 2013
Parragon
Chartist House
15–17 Trim Street
Bath BA1 1HA, UK
www.parragon.com

ISBN 978-1-4723-0561-9

Printed in China

# Beauty and the Beast

Bath • New York • Singapore • Hong Kong • Cologne • Delhi
Melbourne • Amsterdam • Johannesburg • Shenzhen

Once upon a time, a selfish young prince
refused to give an old beggar-woman shelter
in his castle. But the old woman was really an
enchantress. As punishment, she turned the
Prince into a terrifying beast and cast a spell
on everyone in the castle.

Giving the Beast a magic rose she said,
"This will bloom until your twenty-first year.
If you learn to love another and earn that
person's love before the last petal falls, the
spell will be broken. If not, you will remain a
beast forever."

In a sleepy village nearby, an eccentric inventor
named Maurice lived with his beautiful daughter Belle.
Gaston, a strong and handsome young man from the
village, had decided that he wanted to make Belle his wife.
"After all," he told his friend Lefou, "she's the
best-looking girl in town.

Gaston arrived at Belle's house, confident that Belle would agree to marry him. But, when he asked her, Belle refused him without a second thought.

She knew she could never marry someone as arrogant and conceited as Gaston!

One day Maurice set off for a fair with his latest invention. As night fell he lost his way and had to seek refuge in the Beast's castle.

Maurice was welcomed by some friendly, enchanted servants, including a candelabra named Lumiere, a clock named Cogsworth, a teapot named Mrs Potts and her son Chip, a teacup.

But the Beast was furious when he discovered a stranger in his home and he threw Maurice into the dungeon. When Maurice's horse returned home alone, Belle set off at once to search for her father.

"Oh, Papa," Belle cried when she found Maurice in the freezing dungeon, "we must get you out of here!"

Sensing danger, Belle turned round. There was the Beast, towering over her and growling loudly.

"Please let my father go," Belle pleaded. "I'll take his place here."

The Beast agreed straight away. He dragged Maurice out of the cell and sent him back to the village.

The Beast showed Belle to her room.

"You can go anywhere in the castle," he told her, "except the West Wing. That is forbidden!"

Poor Belle was miserable! She missed her father and her home. The enchanted objects prepared a wonderful meal for her and tried to make her happy with their singing and dancing.

But Belle was still lonely and later that night she wandered through the castle. She soon found herself in the West Wing. There, among broken furniture and cracked mirrors, she found the magic rose, its petals drooping sadly.

Just as Belle reached out to touch the rose, the Beast burst in howling with rage. Terrified, Belle ran out into the snowy night.

Belle leapt on to her father's horse and set off blindly into the
dark forest.

Suddenly, she was surrounded by a pack of vicious, hungry
wolves. Just as the wolves closed in for the kill, the Beast appeared
through the trees. Fighting bravely, he drove the wolves away.

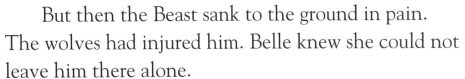

But then the Beast sank to the ground in pain.
The wolves had injured him. Belle knew she could not
leave him there alone.

She took the Beast back to the castle and gently
tended his bleeding wounds. He seemed quite different
now and she was no longer frightened of him.

Meanwhile, at the village tavern, Gaston was still brooding over Belle, even though his friends did their best to cheer him up.

Suddenly, the door burst open and Maurice raced in.

"Help!" he cried. "Belle is being held prisoner by a monstrous beast!"

The men in the tavern burst out laughing. They thought Maurice was mad!

But Gaston smiled to himself. He had thought of a way to
make Belle marry him! He called a tall, sinister-looking man over
to his table and Gaston began to tell him what he had in mind.

As the days passed, Belle and the Beast spent more and more time together. The enchanted servants were delighted. They were certain that Belle would fall in love with their master and break the spell. But time was running out. Each day more petals fell from the magic rose.

One evening, after dining and dancing together, the Beast and Belle sat out on the terrace in the cool night air.

"Are you happy here, Belle?" asked the Beast.

"Yes," replied Belle. "I just wish I could see my father again."

"You can," said the Beast, and he gave Belle a magic mirror. "This will show you whatever you wish."

"Oh, thank you!" exclaimed Belle. But, as she gazed into it, Belle saw her father lost and trembling with cold as he searched for Belle!

Although the Beast loved Belle, he knew he had to let her go to her father. "Take the mirror with you," he said sadly, "so you can remember me."

Belle set off from the castle and soon found Maurice. She brought him safely home and put him to bed.

The next day Gaston arrived at Belle's house with a crowd of villagers. He said that Maurice would be taken to an asylum unless Belle agreed to marry him.

"My father's not mad!" cried Belle.

"He must be," said Lefou, "he was raving about a monstrous beast!"

"The Beast is real!" cried Belle. "Look!" She held up the magic mirror and the crowd saw the Beast for themselves. They all shouted with fear and refused to listen to Belle when she told them the Beast was kind and good.

The men marched up to the castle doors and broke them down. Cogsworth led the enchanted servants in a brave defence of the castle. But the Beast missed Belle and was too heartbroken to fight, even when Gaston beat him with a club and drove him on to the castle roof.

Only when he heard Belle's voice did the Beast look up.
"You came back!" he cried, rushing to embrace Belle.
This was the chance Gaston had been waiting for.
Drawing his dagger, he stabbed the Beast in the back. But as
the Beast collapsed, Gaston tripped – and fell tumbling from
the roof.

Belle ran to the wounded Beast and bent to kiss him.
The last petal was just about to fall from the rose.

"You can't die," sobbed Belle. "I love you! I wish I had
never left you alone!"

Suddenly, a magic mist surrounded the Beast and, before Belle's astonished eyes, he changed into the handsome young prince he had once been.

One by one, the enchanted servants became human again. Weeping with joy, they hugged each other as the Prince swept Belle into his arms.

The Prince had found his true love at last and the spell of the enchantress was broken. As the sun burst through the clouds, they knew they would all live together in happiness forever after.

# The End

Now close the book and *flip it over* for some spellbinding activity fun!

Now, close the book and *flip it over* to read the enchanting story of **Beauty and the Beast**.

# Count the Beauty

How many times is Belle hidden
in this snowy scene?

Answer:

Answer:
Six times

# Wordsearch

The enchanted objects dance and sing to cheer Belle up. How many times can you find the word DISHES in this wordsearch? Circle the words when you find them.

**Tip:** Look up, down and across.

| D | I | S | H | E | S | X | O |
|---|---|---|---|---|---|---|---|
| F | T | A | P | Z | Y | D | L |
| R | D | Y | Z | H | J | I | X |
| Z | I | L | C | B | U | S | N |
| U | S | X | G | K | A | H | A |
| Q | H | D | I | S | H | E | S |
| P | E | R | L | C | M | S | Y |
| L | S | J | W | Z | B | Y | T |

Answer:

Four times

# Time to Colour

Colour in Belle and her enchanted friends.

# Who is Missing?

Complete this puzzle by choosing the correct character for each blank square. Each character should appear only once in each box, row and column.

Answers:

# Dot-to-dot

Join the dots to find out who this arrogant suitor is, then colour him in.

Start here!

# Chip's Bedtime

Mrs Potts needs to put Chip to bed, but she's lost him in the castle. Help her through the maze to find him.

Answer:

# Draw the Beast

Using the grid below as a guide, copy the Beast on the opposite page.

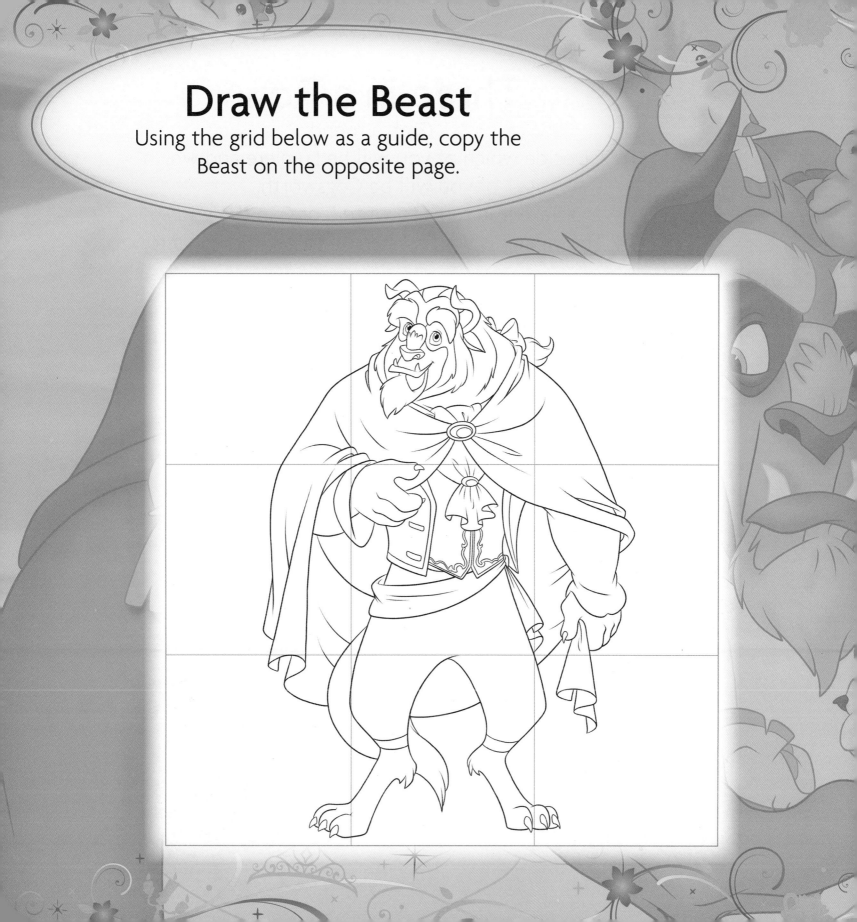

# Three in a Row

1. Grab a friend.
2. Decide which of you will be Lumiere and which of you will be Cogsworth.
3. Take it in turns to write L or C in the grid.
4. The winner is the first person to get three in a row.

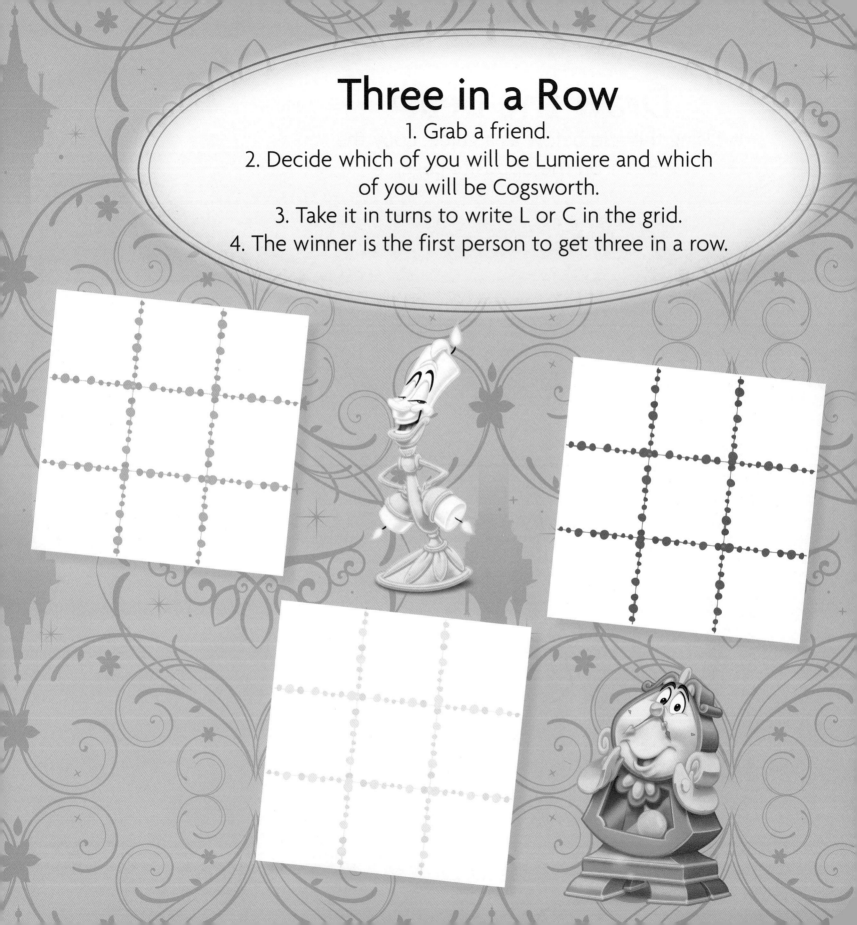

# Colour by Numbers

Belle is ready for her next adventure.
Follow the colour code to complete this
picture of Belle.

# Enchanted Objects

All of the servants have turned into household objects.
If you were under a spell what would you turn into?
Draw it here.

Will you be a
kitchen object?

Make sure you give your
object a face and arms.

What would
your job be?

# Who Comes Next?

Which character comes next in the sequence?
Write the correct letter in the box.

| Belle |
| castle |
| beast |
| friends |
| prince |

Belle lived in a small village, where she spent her time reading and dreaming of adventure.

Her father, Maurice, got lost in the woods on his way to a fair. He stumbled upon a large castle.

The owner was a prince who had been turned into a beast by an enchantress. The Beast took Maurice as his prisoner.

When Belle came to his rescue, she agreed to stay in exchange for her father's freedom. Whilst in the castle, Belle met many enchanted friends.

Over time, Belle and the Beast fell in love. This broke the spell and turned the Beast back into the prince. They lived happily ever after.

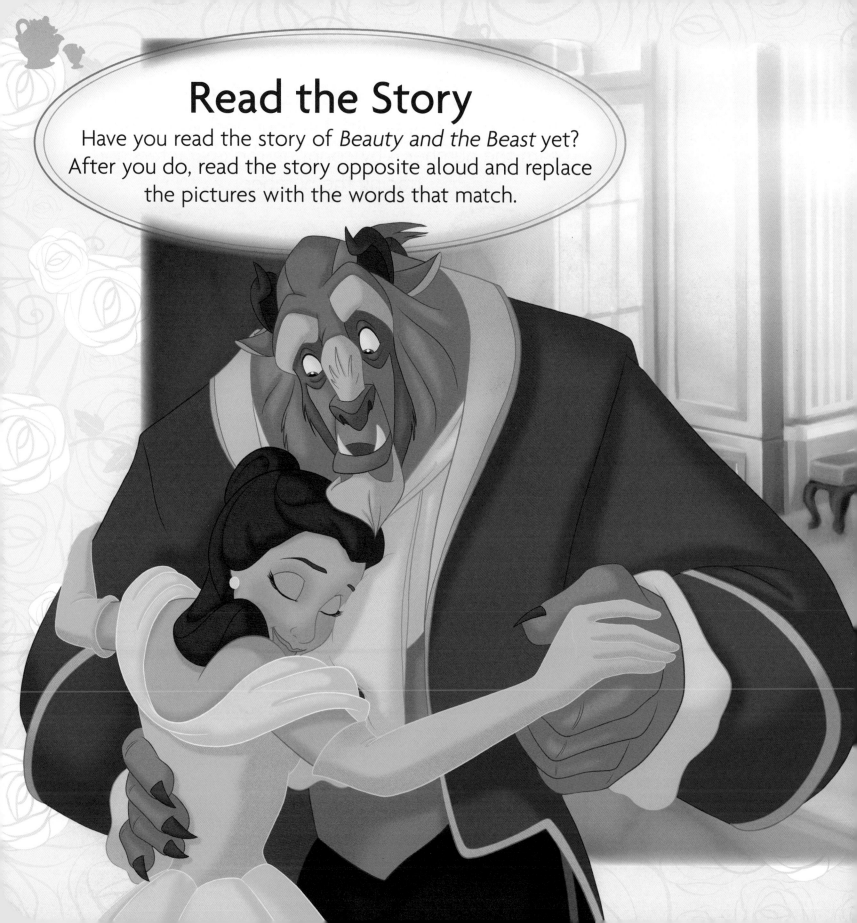

# Read the Story

Have you read the story of *Beauty and the Beast* yet?
After you do, read the story opposite aloud and replace
the pictures with the words that match.

# The Number 4

Belle is spending time with her four enchanted friends. Learn the number 4 by counting the characters and tracing the number.

# Homeward Bound

Belle has been out picking flowers, but she has wandered too far away from the castle and can't find her way back. Can you help her through the maze and get her home?

Answer:

# Magic Mirror

Draw your own dream ballgown
in the magic mirror.

What colour
will it be?

Will it have
a bow?

Will it have a
long train?

# Time to Colour

Now that she has the perfect outfit, Belle is ready to spend the evening dining and dancing with the Beast. Colour them in.

# Spot the Difference

Belle loves being outside with nature. Find the five differences between these two pictures.

# Princess Puzzle

Belle is looking for the perfect dress for her date with the Beast. Complete the puzzle by matching the pieces at the bottom of the page to the gaps in this picture.

1

2

3

4

5

# The Letter B

Belle is going to help you learn to write the letter B. Read the letter aloud and then use the guides to help you write the letter.

## B
### is for
# Belle

# Tangled Lines

The Beast needs to get to the enchanted rose before the last petal falls. Which path will take him to the rose?

1

2

3

Answer: 2

# Magical Friends

The enchanted castle is full of wonderful characters.
Can you match up the close-ups to each character?

A

B

C

D

E

1

2

3

4

5

Answers:
1-B; 2-E; 3-D; 4-C; 5-A

# Look and Find

Lumiere was turned into a candelabra. He is always trying to keep everyone happy. But his flame has gone out in one picture on this page.
Find and circle it.

# Match the Teapot

Mrs Potts and her children were turned into a teaset when the castle fell under the spell. Which shadow matches this picture of her exactly?

1

2

3

4

Answer: 3

# Wordsearch

Belle thinks the Beast's castle is enchanting. How many times can you find the word CASTLE in this wordsearch? Circle the words when you find them.

**Tip:** *Look up, down and across.*

| C | A | S | T | L | E | X | D |
|---|---|---|---|---|---|---|---|
| A | Z | U | D | N | Y | P | B |
| S | X | C | T | F | O | V | C |
| T | C | A | S | T | L | E | A |
| L | G | S | Z | G | V | Y | S |
| E | K | T | W | G | K | F | T |
| F | Z | L | O | P | J | L | L |
| O | P | E | M | T | R | A | E |

Answer:

| C | A | S | T | L | E | X | D |
|---|---|---|---|---|---|---|---|
| A | Z | U | D | N | Y | P | B |
| S | X | C | T | F | O | V | C |
| T | C | A | S | T | L | E | A |
| L | G | S | Z | G | V | Y | S |
| E | K | T | W | G | K | F | T |
| F | Z | L | O | P | J | L | L |
| O | P | E | M | T | R | A | E |

Five times

# Odd One Out

Cogsworth is the Beast's loyal butler. He was turned into a clock when the castle fell under a spell. Only one of the below pictures is the real Cogsworth. Can you find him?
*Hint: he is different from all the others.*

Answer:

# Copy Colouring

Belle is a clever, caring girl who loves to read about adventure. Use this picture as a guide to colour in Belle on the opposite page.

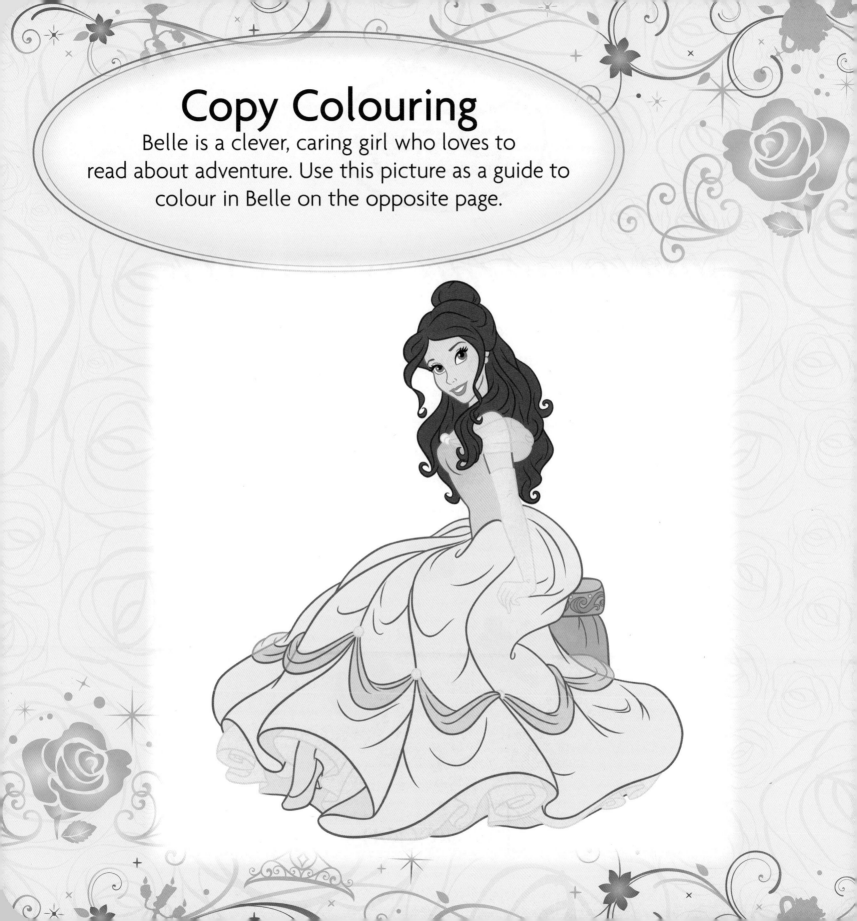

# Disney PRINCESS

# *Spellbinding* Activities

Complete the activities, then flip the book over to read
the enchanting story of Beauty and the Beast.

# PaRragon

Bath • New York • Singapore • Hong Kong • Cologne • Delhi
Melbourne • Amsterdam • Johannesburg • Shenzhen